What-a-Mess in Autumn

Frank Muir
Illustrated by Joseph Wright

First published in 1982 by Ernest Benn Limited,
25 New Street Square, London EC4A 3JA
© Frank Muir 1982
Illustrations © Joseph Wright 1982
ISBN 0 510 00126-2
Printed by South China Printing Co., Hong Kong

Ernest Benn
LONDON

The puppy What-a-Mess had never seen such rain before in his whole short, fat, scruffy life. It seemed to rain all day, every day. Not the fun sort of rain that he was used to; heavy rain which you could see coming down and bouncing up again and you could try to catch in your teeth. And you got soaking wet and went all thin and could play at being a greyhound.

This was like a dull grey cloud. It hung in the air and got in your ears and made you feel sticky all over.

The puppy jumped up and stared through the window at the damp, dripping world outside so that he could give his mother a weather-report.

"It's sogging again," he announced gloomily.

"It's *what?*" said his mother, a little startled.

"Sogging. It's a word I invented last night. Sog is rain that doesn't fall but just hangs about and makes everything soggy."

"You're sitting in a plate of fried-egg," said his mother.

What-a-Mess jumped down and rubbed his hind-quarters against the wallpaper to get some of the yolk off before taking his morning exercise in the garden.

The puppy did not enjoy his walk. It was hard going.

"Sog, sog, sog, sog," went his four paws as he wandered over the waterlogged lawn looking for an old tennis-ball to eat.

"Sog-gwollop, sog-flup, sog-sloop, sog-gloog," went his paws as he picked his way through the cabbages in the kitchen-garden. His paws became tremendously heavy and they seemed to grow wet, black boxing-gloves. As he could scarcely walk by this time he decided to go for a quick tour of the drawing-room carpet to get rid of the mud before attempting his next job which was chasing the cat-next-door.

The mud on his paws was stickier than he thought and he
had to walk several times through his drinking bowl and scrape his
paws against the curtains before he was at fighting weight,
ready to tackle the cat.

Cat chasing is a difficult and dangerous sport, even to a noble Afghan Hound on a dry day. To a plump, damp puppy on a soaking-wet morning it is hazardous indeed. The puppy peered carefully round each corner of the house before he finally caught sight of the cat through the sog. She was sitting still at the end of the drive—probably mouse-spotting—with her back to the puppy. The perfect victim for a shrewd hunter.

What-a-Mess began his run as silently as he could, building up speed with every pace. He was about halfway down the drive and going flat out when the cat turned round and saw him.

This is the moment which every cat chaser dreads. It calls for a quick change of plan. It is necessary to come to a full stop and to stroll off in another direction, whistling, or the chaser is made to look an absolute fool.

What-a-Mess stopped galloping and thrust all four paws forward as brakes. But the drive was covered in a thick, slimy layer of wet leaves and the puppy skidded on at full speed, hurtled past the cat and crashed into the gate, his head jamming between two of the wooden bars.

It was a sad and sore puppy who sat in the shelter of the old barn some hours later and talked things over with the cat.

"I'm fed up with this weather," said What-a-Mess.
"Nothing but sog and wet leaves. How long does it go on for?"

He nibbled the cat's ear and gave it a moody tug.

"They call it 'autumn'," said the cat, giving the puppy a swift right hook to the jaw. "Goes on for weeks. Then there's winter. That's usually worse. Wetter. Colder. You won't like the next few months at all!"

"Excuse me," said a small voice. "Just thought I'd say cheery-bye for the time being. See you both in the spring, when the sun comes out again."

They looked down. It was the hedgehog from the garden shed.

"Time for me to hibernate," went on the hedgehog.
"No more rain and cold. Tuck meself up in me little nest
  underground and be warm again!"

"But how will you eat?" asked the puppy. It was always
  his first worry.

"Don't need to!" said the hedgehog cheerfully. "Be asleep,
  won't I? Well, ta-ra for now. All the very best. Happy days."
  And he was gone.

To sleep away the cold, wet, dreary months! It was the answer. Hibernate.

He had his last meal (he ate everything, including the triangular black biscuits which he hated), explained to his mother that he was hibernating until the spring, asked her to bark at the postman for him and curled himself up in his Hibernation Home for the winter.

What-a-Mess laid his plans carefully. He enlarged the hole he had already begun as a goldmine under a corner of the garden-shed and made it comfortable with two eiderdowns which he dragged down from the bedroom.

He found sleep difficult. A drip of water had begun to fall rhythmically onto the top of his head and he was beginning to feel very cold indeed inside the damp eiderdowns, when the cat suddenly appeared.

"Just came to wish you happy birthday," said the cat, polishing a whisker. "Your first birthday is soon and you'll miss it. Also happy Christmas. You'll miss that too. And happy New Year. That's three parties you'll be missing. By the way, your family's having roast pork tomorrow and you always get a piece of the crackling. I'll taste it for you and let you know what it was like when you wake up. Sweet dreams!" And the cat was gone.

When What-a-Mess's mother went to bed that evening she was not at all surprised to find her puppy in his basket as usual.

"Given up hibernation?" asked his mother.

"Not at all," said the puppy, loftily. "I have decided to become a *part-time* hibernator. Throughout the autumn I intend to hibernate for an hour longer in my basket every morning."

And both of them went happily to sleep.